Contents

The vinegar bottle

There was once an old woman who lived in a
vinegar bottle. She was very unhappy.

"Dear me!" she cried. "How tired I am of living in
this vinegar bottle! If only I lived in a little cottage
in the country with a cow to give me milk. Then I
would be happy!"

Just then, a fairy was flying by. She heard what the old woman said.

"I will make your wish come true," she smiled and she waved her wand. At once the old woman found herself in a dear little cottage. There was a brown cow outside eating the grass.

"Thank you, fairy," said the old woman. "Now I shall be happy."

A week later, the fairy went to see the old woman. "Oh fairy!" she cried. "How unhappy I am living here all alone! If only I lived in a house in the city where I could meet lots of people. Then I would be happy!"

"Very well, I will make your wish come true," said the fairy and she waved her wand. At once the old woman found herself in a fine house in the city. There were lots of people going up and down the street.

"Thank you, fairy," said the old woman. "Now I shall be happy."

A week later, the fairy went to see the old woman.

"Oh fairy!" she cried. "How unhappy I am! The city is so noisy. If only I lived in a quiet house by the sea. Then I would be happy!"

"Very well, I will make your wish come true,"
said the fairy and she waved her wand. At once the
old woman found herself in a quiet house by the sea.

"Thank you, fairy," said the old woman. "Now I
shall be happy."

A week later, the fairy went to see the old woman.

"Oh fairy!" she cried. "How unhappy I am! This house is too small for me. If only I lived in a fine palace up on a hill. Then I would be happy!"

"Very well, I will make your wish come true," said the fairy and she waved her wand. At once the old woman found herself in a beautiful palace high up on the top of a hill.

"Thank you, fairy," said the old woman.
"Now I'm sure I shall be happy."

A week later, the fairy went to see the old woman.

"Oh fairy!" she cried. "How unhappy I am! This palace is too big for me to live in."

Before she could say another word, the fairy waved her wand.

At once, the old woman found herself back in the vinegar bottle.

"Nothing I do can make you happy," said the fairy, "so there you must stay." And she flew away to her own little home in the forest.

One-eyed Jack

One-eyed Jack, the pirate chief,

Was a terrible, fearsome ocean thief.

He wore a peg

Upon one leg;

He wore a hook –

And a dirty look!

One-eyed Jack, the pirate chief –

A terrible, fearsome ocean thief!

Traditional

13

The boy and the wolf

A boy was sitting on a rock on a hill. His sheep were eating the grass.

"Why do I have to sit here and watch the sheep all day?" he asked. "It is no fun out here alone."

The boy saw two men coming up the hill. He wanted to have some fun.

"Help! Help!" he shouted. "A wolf is going to eat my sheep!"

"Where is the wolf?" asked the first man. "Which way did he go?"

"Follow me," said the boy, and the men did. They went to the top of the hill.

"I see many sheep, but where is the wolf?" asked the second man.

"There is no wolf. I played a trick on you," said the boy, and he laughed.

The men were angry with the boy, and they went away. But the boy thought it was fun. He wanted to play the trick again, so he ran after the men.

"Help me! Help me!" he shouted. "A big wolf is hiding by that tree! This is no trick! The wolf is going to eat my sheep!"

"Maybe there is a wolf this time," said the man to his friend. They went up the hill again, but there was no wolf.

"You have tricked us again," said the men.

"But this is the last time. We are going, and we will

not come back." The men walked down the hill

again.

The boy was alone again.

"That was great fun," he said, and he laughed.

"I think I will sit down for a rest."

Just then, a wolf came over the hill.

"My, what beautiful white sheep," said the wolf. "They look good to eat!"

The boy jumped up.

"No!" he shouted. "You can't eat my sheep!"

"The men have gone," said the wolf. "There is no one here to stop me. Which one will be first?"

The boy ran to the top of the hill.

"Help!" he shouted. "Please help me. The wolf has come, and he is going to eat my beautiful sheep!"

The men said, "That boy is playing tricks again. We know there is no wolf."

"Please come!" said the boy. "This time there **is** a wolf!"

"You see?" said the wolf. "Now no one will help you. That's what you get for playing tricks!"

The little red hen

There was once a little red hen. She lived in a cottage in the forest. Every morning she took a brush and swept her little house until it was clean and bright. When her work was done, the little red hen took her basket and went out to get sticks for her fire.

One day, a fox came walking through the forest. He saw the little red hen's cottage. He looked through the window and saw that the house was empty. He thought he would try to catch the little red hen when she came home so he went and hid behind a tree.

After a while he saw the little red hen coming along the forest path with her basket of sticks.

When the little red hen came near, the fox jumped out from behind the tree. The little red hen was very frightened but quickly she flew up into a tree where the fox couldn't get her.

Now the fox was angry, but he thought of a clever way to get the little red hen down from the tree. He began to chase his tail! Round and round and round he went.

The little red hen looked down at the fox going round and round. She began to feel dizzy, and before long, she felt so dizzy that she fell down from the tree.

Now the fox could catch her, but when he tried to run over to her, he felt dizzy too and fell over. The little red hen jumped up and ran into her cottage. She shut the door with a bang.

So the fox didn't catch the little red hen after all.

An old woman

There was an old woman tossed up in a basket,

Seventeen times as high as the moon.

Where she was going I couldn't but ask it,

For in her hand she carried a broom.

"Old woman, old woman, old woman," quoth I,

"Where are you going to up so high?"

"To brush the cobwebs off the sky!"

"May I come with you?" "Aye, by-and-by."

Traditional

The Wind and the Sun

The Wind was very strong.

He was the North Wind, and he could blow across the hills and across the sea. He could make a storm blow up and he could make brave men frightened.

The Sun was very strong.

She was the mighty Sun, and she could shine in the sky all day. She could make the trees green and she could make the rivers laugh.

"I'm stronger than you," said the North Wind.
He blew a big strong wind. It whistled through space
and blew an old woman into a fence ."I'm stronger
than you, little Sun."

"Is that what you think, North Wind?" said the
Sun. "You think you are as strong as the mighty
Sun? We shall see about that."

She looked down from the sky.

"Do you see a man," she said, "walking along
the road?"

"Yes," said the North Wind. "I see him."

"Now we'll find out who's stronger," said the Sun.
"If you can make that man take his coat off,
you will win. But if I can make him take his coat off,
I shall win. I shall be stronger than you."

The North Wind laughed.

"Oh, little Sun," he said. "What sort of competition is that? I shall blow that man's coat off in a second."

The Sun smiled. "Why don't you have first try, then, North Wind? Let me see what you can do."

"Very well," said the North Wind. "Keep back, everyone. Give me space to blow."

And so the North Wind began to blow. He blew as he had never blown before. He blew and blew and blew.

The man on the road looked up. What a terrible wind! He pulled his coat right round him.

"I'll blow that coat **offFFFFFF**," shouted the North Wind. He called up a terrible storm of rain and snow. "I'll blow it right **offFFFFFF...**"

But the man only pulled his coat tighter and tighter round him.

"You need a rest, North Wind," said the Sun. "You must be tired. Now it is time for me to try." And so the North Wind stopped. The rain and the snow stopped. And the Sun came out.

The man looked up. "How good the sun feels after the storm," he said. "How good it feels on my back."

The Sun said nothing. She just shone. She shone and shone and shone.

"It feels so good," said the man. And in no time at all, he stopped and took off his coat.

The Sun and the North Wind looked at the man,
walking along the road with his coat in his hand.

"How happy he looks," said the Sun. She smiled
at the North Wind. "You are very strong, North
Wind," she said. "But to blow and blow on people is
not a good way to make them do what you want."

"No," said the North Wind. "I see that now.
And I see now, oh mighty Sun, which of us is
the stronger."